When Kerry woke up it was still dark. She felt excited but she couldn't remember why. She could hear Mum, Dad and Grandad talking and laughing in the kitchen.

"Now I remember!" said Kerry. "We're going on holiday today!" She put on her dressing gown and went downstairs.

"Ah, there you are," said Grandad. "I thought you were never going to wake up, Kerry."

Dad was packing a large cardboard box with all the food they would need for the first few days.

"We must make an early start," he said. "There will be lots of holiday traffic if we leave it any later."

"You'll have to get your own breakfast, Kerry," said Mum. "I've still got to pack the big case, and get Max dressed." Max was Kerry's little brother.

Kerry found a choc-ice in the freezer.

"I'm too excited for a proper breakfast," she thought.

“I wish you were coming with us, Grandad,” said Kerry. “Won’t you change your mind?”

“No, thank you,” smiled Grandad. “I’m looking forward to some peace and quiet. It will make a nice change.”

Mum came downstairs with the big case. Max and Bubbles helped her to carry it. Bubbles was Max's teddy.

"Bubbles want drink. Bubbles want breakfast," said Max. Dad gave Max his breakfast.

“I think we’re ready to go now,” said Mum. “Dad has packed the food and I’ve packed the luggage. Kerry, can you check that you have everything you need? Make sure Max doesn’t forget Bubbles.”

Dad put Max in the baby-seat in the back of the car. He fell asleep almost at once.

"That's a bit of luck," said Dad.

"I still don't see why we have to leave so early," said Kerry. "Nobody else is awake yet."

"I told you," said Dad. "We're going to miss all the traffic. The sooner we leave, the sooner we'll get there. So let's get going."

"Are you sure you won't change your mind and come with us, Grandad?" asked Mum.

"Quite sure," replied Grandad. "Have a lovely time."

It was beginning to get light as they drove through the streets of the town.

"You see," said Dad, "we've missed all the traffic. We'll be in Devon in no time."

"Dad, I need to go to the toilet," said Kerry.

"Didn't you remember to go before we left?" said Mum.

Just then Max woke up.

"Bubbles want potty," he wailed. "Max want potty."

"Bubbles will just have to wait," groaned Dad, "and so will Max and Kerry. We can stop at the first service station on the motorway."

There was a lot of traffic on the motorway.

"I thought you said there would be no traffic if we set off early," said Kerry.

"Everybody must have had the same idea," said Dad.

"Bubbles bursting!" wailed Max. At last they reached the service station.

Everybody except Max cheered up when they got to the cottage.

“I’ll light a big fire,” said Dad. “Then we’ll have something to eat. I don’t know about the rest of you, but I’m starving.”

“Bubbles hungry. Bubbles gone!” sobbed Max.

"We can't unpack the car yet," said Mum. "It's raining too hard."

"Once I get this fire going," said Dad. "I'll dash outside and bring the food in. That's all we need for now."

Dad went to the car. He was gone for a long time. When he came back he had a strange look on his face.

"Where's the food?" asked Mum.

"There is no food," said Dad quietly. "I'm afraid I must have left it at home."

"Oh no!" groaned Mum. "I knew that I should have checked everything before we left. The shops are closed now so we can't buy any food. At least there are a few packets of biscuits in the big case. I'll go and get them."

It was still raining heavily. Mum dashed out to the car to fetch the big suitcase.

She was gone for a very long time. When she came back she had a strange look on her face.

"Did you get the biscuits?" asked Dad.

"No," said Mum. "The case wasn't there. I was sure I had remembered everything. I don't know how it got left behind."

"What else was in the big suitcase?" asked Kerry.

"All the clothes we need for the holiday," said Mum quietly.

"There's only one thing to do now," said Dad. "We'll have to go out and get something to eat at a cafe tonight. Tomorrow we'll have to go home."

"We'll have to run to the car or we'll all be soaked," said Mum. Dad and Kerry ran and Mum carried Max. When they were all in the car Dad started the engine, but the car wouldn't move.

"That's strange," said Dad.

"Did you remember to put petrol in?" asked Kerry.

"No," whispered Dad. "I don't believe I did."

"There's nothing we can do," said Mum. "Back into the house everyone."

Everybody sat around the fire. They were tired, wet and very hungry. There was a knock at the door.

"Who could that be?" said Mum.

"Bubbles!" shouted an excited Max.

"I shouldn't think so," said Dad.

"I'll see," said Kerry going to the door. It was Grandad.

"I changed my mind," he said. "I thought I'd take a bit of a holiday after all. I also thought you might need this case of clothes and all this food."

"Oh Grandad, we're so pleased to see you," said Kerry.

"You've saved the day!" laughed Mum.

"Bubbles lost," sobbed Max.

"No he isn't," said Grandad. "I met him in the service station so I gave him a lift."